GARFIELD

Classics

Volume Thirteen

MY THIRTEENTH CLASSIC COLLECTION
CONTAINS:

SHOVE AT FIRST SIGHT

TO EAT, OR NOT TO EAT?

DOUBLE TROUBLE

JIM DAVIS

ℛ

First published by Ravette Publishing 2004.

Printed and bound in Great Britain
for Ravette Publishing Limited,
Unit 3, Tristar Centre,
Star Road, Partridge Green,
West Sussex RH13 8RA

by Cox & Wyman, Reading, Berkshire.

ISBN: 1 84161 206 5

Garfield

Shove At
First Sight

JIM DAVIS

JIM DAVIS 10-20

I'M PRACTICING LOOKING INNOCENT

© 1995 PAWS, INC./Distributed by Universal Press Syndicate

GARFIELD, WOULD YOU HAPPEN TO KNOW WHO EMPTIED THE REFRIGERATOR?

WITH A FACE LIKE THIS?

JIM DAVIS 11-9

© 1995 PAWS, INC./Distributed by Universal Press Syndicate

© 1995 PAWS, INC./Distributed by Universal Press Syndicate

© 1995 PAWS, INC./Distributed by Universal Press Syndicate

JIM DAVIS 12-30

© 1996 PAWS, INC./Distributed by Universal Press Syndicate

© 1996 PAWS, INC./Distributed by Universal Press Syndicate

© 1996 PAWS, INC./Distributed by Universal Press Syndicate

© 1996 PAWS, INC./Distributed by Universal Press Syndicate

TAP
TAP

© 1996 PAWS, INC./Distributed by Universal Press Syndicate

JIM DAVIS 2-8

Garfield

To Eat Or Not To Eat?

(That is a silly question!)

JIM DAVIS

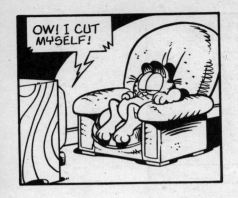

© 1996 PAWS, INC./Distributed by Universal Press Syndicate

HOW COME I JUST SAW A MOUSE RUNNING ACROSS THIS TABLE?!

NORMALLY YOU WOULDN'T

BUT FAT EDDIE'S PRETTY SLOW

JIM DAVIS 3-5

© 1996 PAWS, INC./Distributed by Universal Press Syndicate

© 1996 PAWS, INC./Distributed by Universal Press Syndicate

© 1996 PAWS, INC./Distributed by Universal Press Syndicate

© 1996 PAWS, INC./Distributed by Universal Press Syndicate

© 1996 PAWS, INC./Distributed by Universal Press Syndicate

JIM DAVIS 5-9

© 1996 PAWS, INC./Distributed by Universal Press Syndicate

© 1996 PAWS, INC.Distributed by Universal Press Syndicate

JIM DAVIS 6-27

© 1996 PAWS, INC./Distributed by Universal Press Syndicate

JIM DAVIS 6-28

GRAB!

© 1996 PAWS, INC. Distributed by Universal Press Syndicate

PLOOP!

AS YOU CAN SEE, DOGS AREN'T THE ONLY ONES WHO CAN FETCH SLIPPERS

I HATE YOU

Garfield

Double Trouble

© PAWS

JIM DAVIS

ℛℛ

© PAWS

© 1996 PAWS, INC./Distributed by Universal Press Syndicate

FLING!

JIM DAVIS 7-23

© 1996 PAWS, INC./Distributed by Universal Press Syndicate

© 1996 PAWS, INC. Distributed by Universal Press Syndicate

YOU'RE OUT OF FRUIT! WHAT ARE YOU GOING TO DO?!

JIM DAVIS 8-15

© 1996 PAWS, INC./Distributed by Universal Press Syndicate

GONK!

© 1996 PAWS, INC./Distributed by Universal Press Syndicate

© 1996 PAWS, INC./Distributed by Universal Press Syndicate

SWAT

JIM DAVIS 9-11

© 1996 PAWS, INC./Distributed by Universal Press Syndicate

© 1996 PAWS, INC./Distributed by Universal Press Syndicate

© 1996 PAWS, INC./Distributed by Universal Press Syndicate

TAP
TAP

EEEK!

JIM DAVIS 10-30

JIM DAViS 11-2

JIM DAVIS 11-7

OTHER GARFIELD BOOKS AVAILABLE

Pocket Books	**Price**	**ISBN**
Below Par	£3.50	1 84161 152 2
Bon Appetit	£3.50	1 84161 038 0
Compute This!	£3.50	1 84161 194 8
Double Trouble	£3.50	1 84161 008 9
Eat My Dust	£3.50	1 84161 098 4
Fun in the Sun	£3.50	1 84161 097 6
Goooooooal!	£3.50	1 84161 037 2
Great Impressions	£3.50	1 85304 191 2
I Don't Do Perky	£3.50	1 84161 195 6
In Training	£3.50	1 85304 785 6
Light Of My Life	£3.50	1 85304 353 2
On The Right Track	£3.50	1 85304 907 7
Pop Star	£3.50	1 84161 151 4
To Eat, Or Not To Eat?	£3.50	1 85304 991 3
Wave Rebel	£3.50	1 85304 317 6
With Love From Me To You	£3.50	1 85304 392 3

new titles available February 2005

No. 49 – S.W.A.L.K.	£3.50	1 84161 225 1
No. 50 – Gotcha!	£3.50	1 84161 226 X

Theme Books		
Guide to Behaving Badly	£4.50	1 85304 892 5
Guide to Cat Napping	£4.50	1 84161 087 9
Guide to Coffee Mornings	£4.50	1 84161 086 0
Guide to Creatures Great & Small	£3.99	1 85304 998 0
Guide to Healthy Living	£3.99	1 85304 972 7
Guide to Pigging Out	£4.50	1 85304 893 3
Guide to Romance	£3.99	1 85304 894 1
Guide to Successful Living	£3.99	1 85304 973 5
Guide to The Seasons	£3.99	1 85304 999 9

new titles now available

Entertains You	£4.50	1 84161 221 9
Slam Dunk!	£4.50	1 84161 222 7

2-in-1 Theme Books		
Easy Does It	£6.99	1 84161 191 3
Licensed to Thrill	£6.99	1 84161 192 1
Out For The Couch	£6.99	1 84161 144 1
The Gruesome Twosome	£6.99	1 84161 143 3

new titles now available

All in Good Taste	£6.99	1 84161 209 X
Lazy Daze	£6.99	1 84161 208 1

Classics	Price	ISBN
Volume One	£5.99	1 85304 970 0
Volume Two	£5.99	1 85304 971 9
Volume Three	£5.99	1 85304 996 4
Volume Four	£5.99	1 85304 997 2
Volume Five	£5.99	1 84161 022 4
Volume Six	£5.99	1 84161 023 2
Volume Seven	£5.99	1 84161 088 7
Volume Eight	£5.99	1 84161 089 5
Volume Nine	£5.99	1 84161 149 2
Volume Ten	£5.99	1 84161 150 6
Volume Eleven	£5.99	1 84161 175 1
Volume Twelve	£5.99	1 84161 176 X

new title now available
Volume Fourteen	£5.99	1 84161 207 3

Little Books		
C-c-c-caffeine	£2.50	1 84161 183 2
Food 'n' Fitness	£2.50	1 84161 145 X
Laughs	£2.50	1 84161 146 8
Love 'n' Stuff	£2.50	1 84161 147 6
Surf 'n' Sun	£2.50	1 84161 186 7
The Office	£2.50	1 84161 184 0
Wit 'n' Wisdom	£2.50	1 84161 148 4
Zzzzzzz	£2.50	1 84161 185 9

Miscellaneous		
Garfield the Movie	£7.99	1 84161 205 7
Garfield 25 years of me!	£7.99	1 84161 173 5
Treasury 4	£10.99	1 84161 180 8
Treasury 3	£9.99	1 84161 142 5

new title now available
Treasury 5	£10.99	1 84161 198 0

All Garfield books are available at your local bookshop or from the publisher at the address below. Just tick the titles required and send the form with your payment to:-

RAVETTE PUBLISHING
Unit 3, Tristar Centre, Star Road, Partridge Green, West Sussex RH13 8RA

Prices and availability are subject to change without notice.
Please enclose a cheque or postal order made payable to **Ravette Publishing** to the value of the cover price of the book and allow the following for UK postage and packing:

60p for the first book + 30p for each additional book
except *Garfield Treasuries* when please add £3.00 per copy for p&p

Name ....

Address ....

....

....